Brother Trouble

by Anna Kenna

illustrated by Fifi Colston

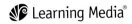 Learning Media®

Contents

1. The Candy Commercial

Last week, my brother and I acted in a TV commercial about Fruity Chews candy.

Our mom works for an advertising agency, so we do quite a few commercials together.

In the candy commercial, I was a kid and Justin was a kangaroo.

At the end of the commercial, Justin hopped up to me in his kangaroo suit. He punched me on the shoulder and ran away with my packet of Fruity Chews.

I turned to the camera and rubbed my shoulder. "Kangaroos love Fruity Chews, too," I said.

"Nice one, kids," said the director. "That's a wrap."

"You didn't have to hit me so hard,"
I said to Justin. "It was *meant* to be a
pretend punch."

"Chill out, sis," said Justin. "It was
meant to look real."

Mom met us at the studio door. "Well done, you two," she said.

She looked at me closely. "Are you OK, Lauren?" she asked. "Your eyes look watery."

"It's Justin's fault," I complained. "He punched me real hard."

Mom gave me a kiss on the forehead. "I'm sure he didn't mean to hurt you," she said.

I sighed. Mom always said that.

2. I Say "No!"

A few weeks later, Mom asked us if we wanted to do another TV commercial together. This one was for Oatie Bites breakfast cereal.

Mom showed us the script.

(Sister is tied to a chair.)

Big Brother *(sitting at table eating Oatie Bites)*: Yummy, yummy, I'm filling my tummy.

(Camera moves to Sister.)

Sister: Hey, that's not fair — I want my share!

Big Brother: No. No way! You don't have a hope. Good thing I have my trusty rope.

(Sister tries to get free while Big Brother eats the Oatie Bites.)

Narrator: You'll have to fight with all your might for your share of Oatie Bites.

When I saw the script, I freaked.
"Why do *I* have to be tied up?" I asked.
"Why does Justin always get the winning part? It's so unfair!"

"I'm not doing it!" I said to Mom. "No way. Never!"

3. Anita's Idea

Mom thought that I would change my mind about doing the commercial, but I didn't.

On the day of the filming, I wouldn't even come out of my room.

Mom came into my room. "Come on, Lauren," she said. "Justin has promised to be good."

"Yeah, right," I said.

Mom asked Dad to talk to me.
"Everyone's counting on you, Lauren,"
he said. "You're letting everyone down."

"But Justin's a big bully!" I said. "He's
always punching me and hurting me,
and you and Mom don't care."

Dad put his hand on my shoulder.
"Of course we care, Lauren."

"Oh, you sound just like Mom!" I said.
"I knew you'd be on Justin's side. You're
a boy, and boys always stick together!"

Dad smiled and stroked his chin.

I got real mad. "What are you smiling for?" I asked.

"No one's called me a boy for a long time," said Dad.

"It's not funny, Dad!" I said. "I'm not doing that dumb commercial, and that's final!"

Just at that moment, the phone rang.
I heard Mom answer it. It was Anita at
the film studio wanting to know where
we were.

Mom brought the phone into my room.
"Anita wants to talk to you," she said.
She held the phone out to me.

I sighed and took the phone. "Hello."

"Hello, Lauren," said Anita. "Your mom has told me the problem, and I've got an idea."

I listened to Anita's idea. I loved it!
"OK, I'll do it," I said.

"Phew!" said Mom and Dad.

4. A Surprise for Justin

Justin practiced his lines all the way to the studio – loudly. "No. No way. You don't have a hope. Good thing I have my trusty rope."

I smiled to myself. I was thinking about Anita's idea.

Anita met us at the studio. "Come through to the dressing room," she said.

Anita winked at me. I winked back.

I put on some pink pajamas. The
hairdresser messed up my hair so that
I looked like I'd just gotten out of bed.

Justin wore blue pajamas. The
hairdresser messed up his hair, too.

When we were ready, Anita took us onto the set.

Justin saw the rope hanging over the back of a chair. He started swinging it around like a lasso.

"Oh," said Anita, "I guess I should tell you. I've changed the script." She gave me and Justin a copy each. "Check it out."

5. A Lesson for Justin

(Big Brother is tied to a chair.)

Sister *(sitting at table eating Oatie Bites)*: Yummy, yummy, I'm filling my tummy.

(Camera moves to Big Brother.)

Big Brother: Hey, that's not fair — I want my share!

Sister: No. No way! You don't have a hope. Good thing I have my trusty rope.

(Big Brother tries to get free while Sister eats the Oatie Bites.)

Narrator: You'll have to fight with all your might for your share of Oatie Bites.

You should have seen the look on Justin's face!

I ate my Oatie Bites as slowly as I could. I had a big smile on my face for the whole commercial. Justin just sat there and sulked.

When we got home, Dad was making dinner. Justin was still sulking when we sat down to eat.

"What's the matter with you?" It was my turn to tease Justin now.

"That's enough, Lauren," said Mom.

Dad looked at Justin and smiled.
"It's not so much fun when the shoe's
on the other foot, is it, son?" he said.

"Or the rope's in the other hand,"
I added.

Mom and Dad laughed when I said that.
I looked at Justin, and he smiled – just
a little bit.

I *think* Justin and I will get along better
now, but I'll have to wait and see.